drawn
by
DAVE BERG

MAD'S

Dave Berg
Looks
at
People

**FOREWORD BY
ALBERT B. FELDSTEIN**

A SIGNET BOOK

N·A·L
SIGNET
BOOKS

Published by
The New American Library,
New York and Toronto
The New English Library Limited, London

SIGNET TRADEMARK REG. U.S. PAT. OFF. AND FOREIGN COUNTRIES
REGISTERED TRADEMARK——MARCA REGISTRADA
HECHO EN CHICAGO, U.S.A.

SIGNET BOOKS are published *in the United States* by
The New American Library, Inc.,
1301 Avenue of the Americas, New York, New York 10019,
in Canada by The New American Library of Canada Limited,
295 King Street East, Toronto 2, Ontario,
in the United Kingdom by The New English Library Limited,
Barnard's Inn, Holborn, London, E.C. 1, England

PRINTED IN THE UNITED STATES OF AMERICA

HOW DAVE BERG DOES IT—

See Page 5!

Also by Dave Berg

FOREWORD

In all the years that we've been running **"The Lighter Side Of_____"** articles in the magazine, no one has ever asked me, "Where does **MAD's** Dave Berg get his funny ideas?" (Of course, a few cranks have asked me, "Where does **MAD** get the idea that Dave Berg is funny?" —but then, you can't please everybody!) And so, to satisfy this mass indifference, I'd like to tell you a little bit about how Dave Berg works for **MAD.** (I could tell you a little bit about *why* Dave Berg works for **MAD,** but that would involve going into a few embarrassing personal experiences, the photos of which Dave keeps in his safe.)

Dave Berg works on the principle that if you steal from books, it's plagiarism . . . but if you steal from people, it's *research*. Which is exactly what he does. He steals ideas from other people. He accomplishes this through the "interview method". (At least, that's the excuse he uses to visit his neighbors' wives while their husbands are away at work.) Dave goes from door to door, asking questions about any and all subjects that might end up as **"Lighter Side"** articles in **MAD.** (He also goes from door to door selling Fuller Brushes, but that's because the prices **MAD** pays for these articles are on **"The Lighter Side".)**

In the course of conducting these interviews, nothing escapes Dave's I.Q. (Inquisitive Quotient). The slightest suggestion, an obscure incident, a casual remark can trigger off the inspiration for a **"Lighter Side"** article. Recently, I observed Dave at a party. While everyone was carrying their drinks, Dave was carrying his note pad. I watched a young man ask Dave for a cigarette, saw him go through a third degree before he got it, and shortly after, was considering the **"Lighter Side Of Smoking"** for **MAD.** Once, a neighbor who remembered Dave from a previous painful interview slammed the door in his face and broke his nose. So **MAD** ended up with **"The Lighter Side Of Doctors"** (or was it **"The Lighter Side Of Broken Noses"?).**

Dave likes to think of himself as a "reporter". The people he's interviewed prefer to think of him as a "pest". These days, no one who comes near the Berg home is safe from his probing queries. That's why, these days, no one comes near the Berg home. Dave's is the only house that gets its mail delivery on the mailman's own time . . . at 2 A.M. in the morning. Which may explain why **MAD's** never run **"The Lighter Side Of Mailmen".** Dave doesn't leave a note for the milkman, he leaves a questionnaire. To sum it up, you could never accuse Dave of begging the question...only of questioning the beggar!

To best illustrate how Dave really works (because so far, this Foreword hasn't really told you anything!), let's look at a typical page from Dave Berg's note pad:

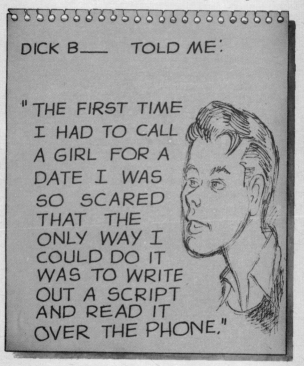

On the following pages, you will see how Dave worked this into a typical **"Berg's Eye View"** cartoon sequence. While you're reading it, I'll take off...before Dave corners me and I end up supplying material for **"The Lighter Side Of Writing Ridiculous Forewords".**

Al Feldstein

✗ (His Mark)

Editor,
MAD Magazine

TELE-PHONY

Hello—Barbara—This—is—Dick Blair—I hope—your—parents—are—well—and—that—this—heat wave—isn't too much—for your—sweet little brother—And speaking about the—heat—ha-ha—I thought—of a nice way—to—cool off—so—if you'd like to go—to the—pool—with—me—tomorrow . . . ?

KID-TYPE PEOPLE

MEASURE FOR MEASURE

CLICK

SMALL TALK

BORN YESTERDAY

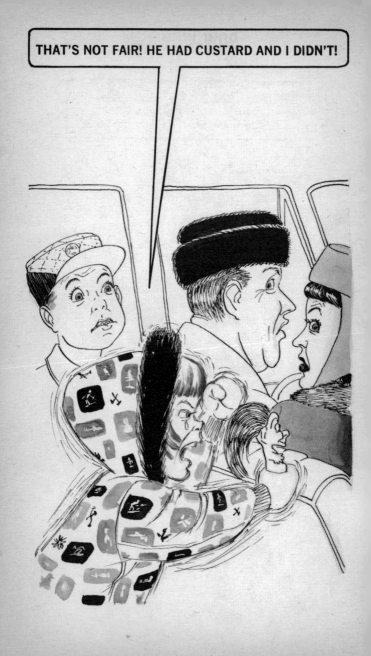

BOW-WOW OUT

DIMINISHING RETURNS

MR. FIXIT

TEENAGE-TYPE
PEOPLE

ROGER
KAPUTNICK
LOVES
~~SYLVIA~~

~~CLAIRE~~
~~IDA~~
~~MARILYN~~
~~LILY~~
~~NAOMI~~
~~RHODA~~
~~MAXINE~~
~~RUTH~~
~~VIRGINIA~~
~~FANNIE~~
ELAINE

THE GUIDING LIGHT

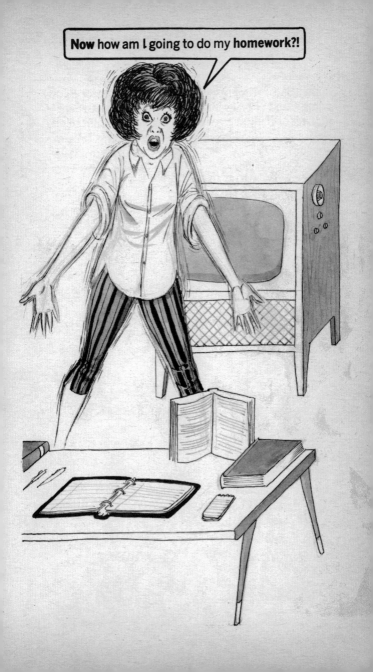

ANSWERING SERVICE

BEAUTY PALLOR

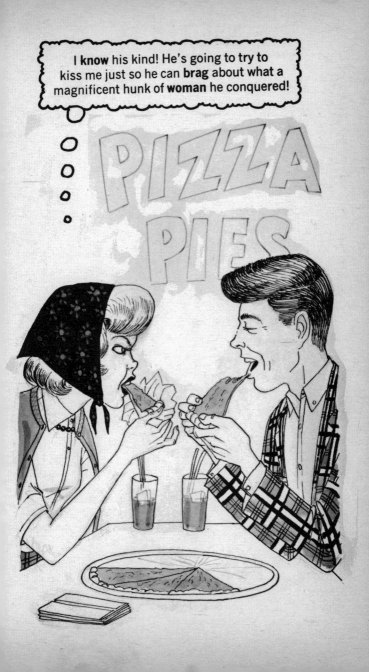

OFF THE CUFF

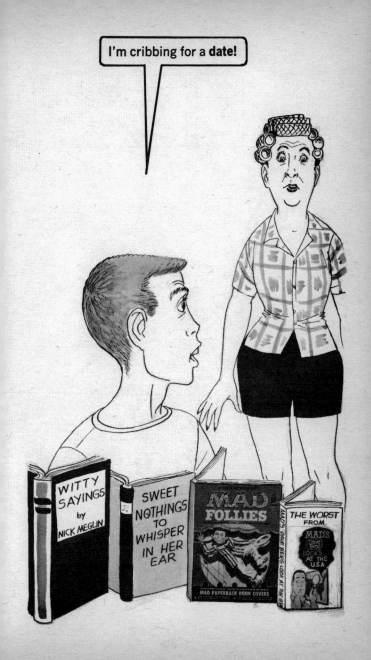

BRACE YOURSELF

PARENT-TYPE PEOPLE

MOM-CONFORMIST

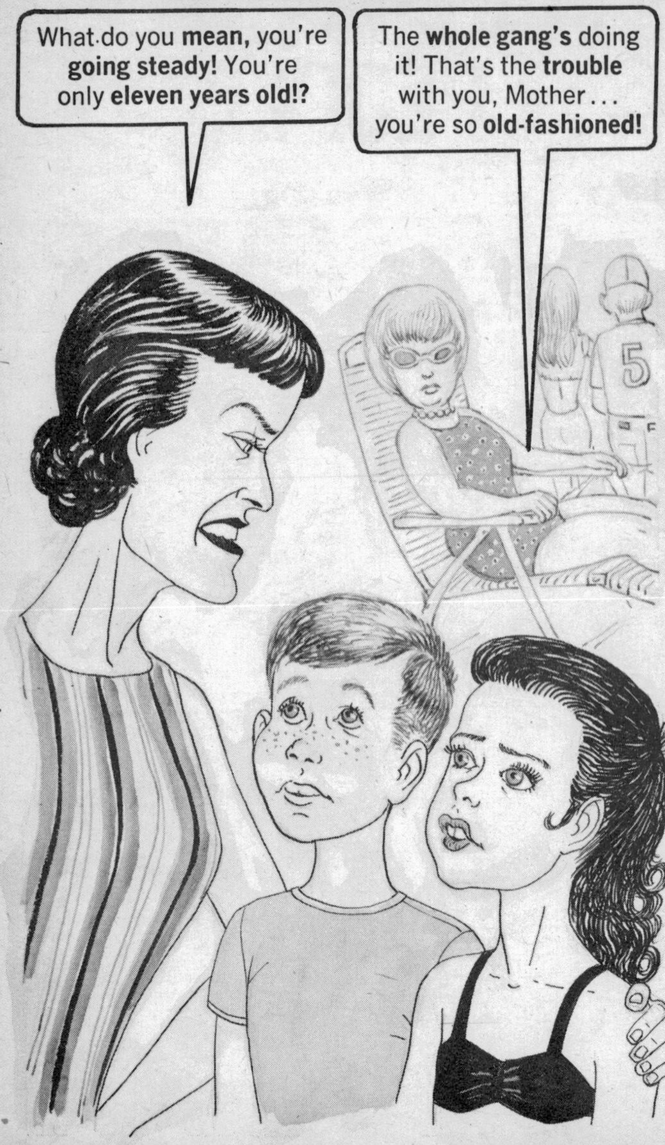

70

GLUTTON FOR PUNISHMENT

COPPING-OUT

PARTY LINE

Boy, I tell you—the **women** in this neighborhood and their **"One-Upmanship"**! It started a couple of months ago when Mrs. Knipling gave a party for **her** little boy and handed out **paddle balls** for **party favors**! Then, Mrs. Lubbox, in order to out-do her, hired a **pony** for **her** kid's party!

MATH HYSTERIA

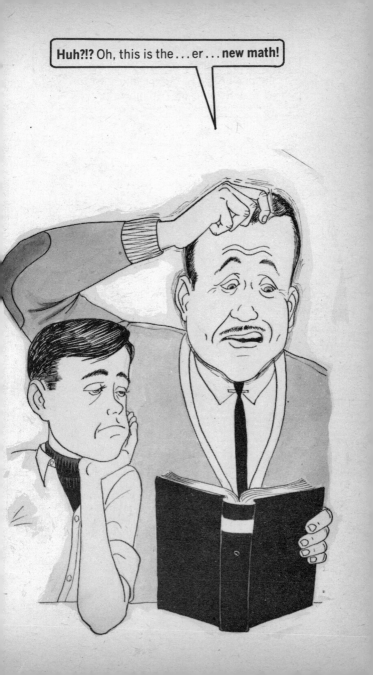

FRIENDLY PERSUASION

SOUND AND FURY

EVERY-DAY-TYPE PEOPLE

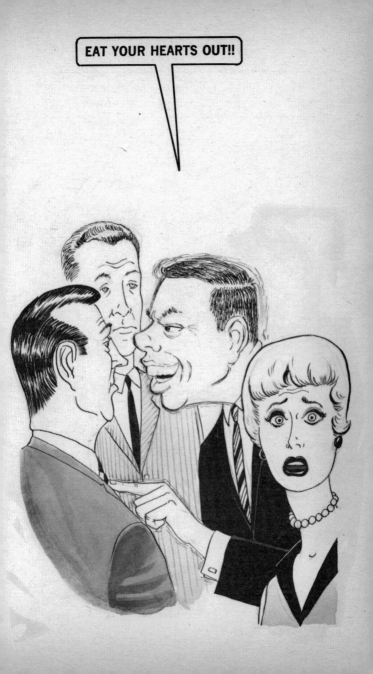

POOLS RUSH IN

TONGUE-IN-CHECK

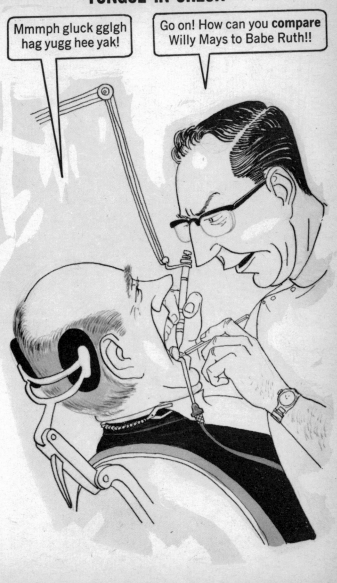

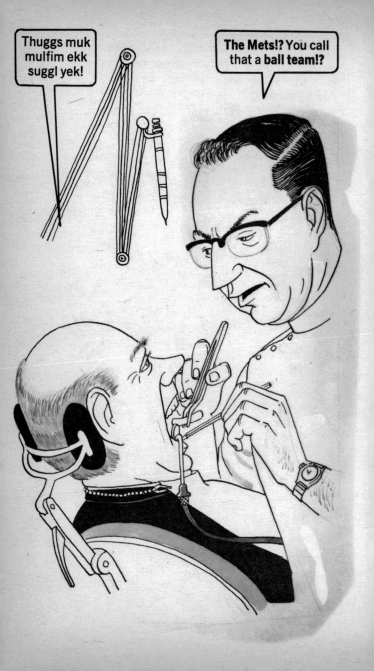

CHAFING DISH

CAUGHT WET-HANDED

Yipe! Does she always have to make such **sharp turns?** . . . There she goes again, driving **too close** to the **car ahead! . . .** So **stop,** already! It's a **"Full Stop"** sign!

IT FIGURES

Look at that brazen young hussy—wearing that Bikini! What's this country **coming** to, anyhow?

AUTO-MOTIVES

FINE PRINT

ORGANIZATION-TYPE PEOPLE

FIRE
BUILDING

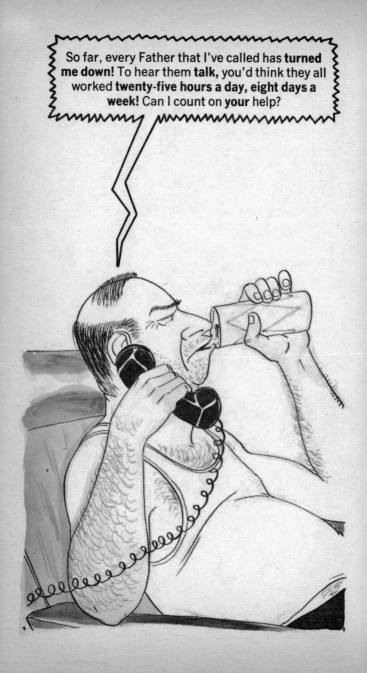

TAKING THE WRAP

For years, all I've **heard** about is the **vicious pettiness of women** . . . how **power-hungry females** join the P.T.A. to **feed** their **ravenous egos** and **vanities** . . . the constant battle of **Parents** against **the Principal** and **the Teachers** . . . the obnoxious competition and fighting among the **cliques!**

And anyhow, you've always made so much noise about how **utterly useless** the whole P.T.A. organization is! So will you tell me **why** in heck you suddenly decided to **go there** tonight?

SPEECH IMPEDIMENT

AIDS TO EDUCATION

NAME_____

ADDRESS_____

PHONE NO._____

I would like to work on the checked
        P. T. A. COMMITTEE

1. Harassing the Board of Education
   Committee___

2. Harassing the School Principal
   Committee...___

3. Harassing the School Teachers
   Committee...___

4. Harassing the School Children
   Committee...___

5. Interfering With The Curriculum
   Committee...___

POLITICAL-TYPE PEOPLE

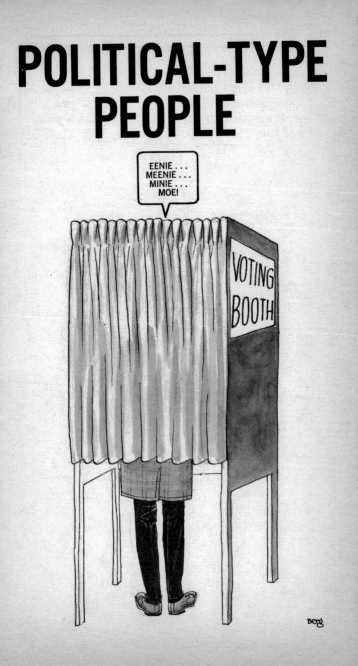

CONSERVATIVE ESTIMATE

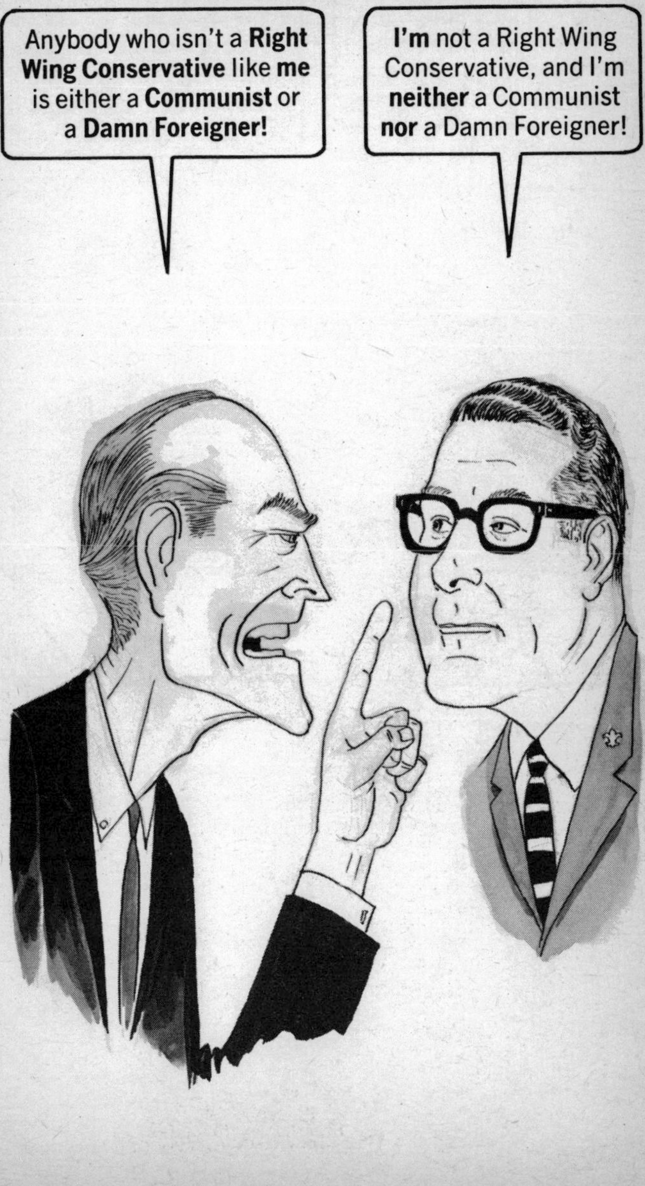

Give me one good reason why **you,** as a supposed **Red-White-And-Blue American,** aren't a Right Wing Conservative!
Because it's an **extreme!** A certain Great Man once wrote about the **"Golden Mean"** in which he said: **Moderation, all things to moderation!"**

WHAT!? Are you out of your minds? Did you ever examine his record? Number one: He's for everything rotten, and against everything good! Number two: He has the worst absentee record in Politics. And number three: The only time he showed up was to vote himself a raise in salary!

CLUTCHING AT STRAWS

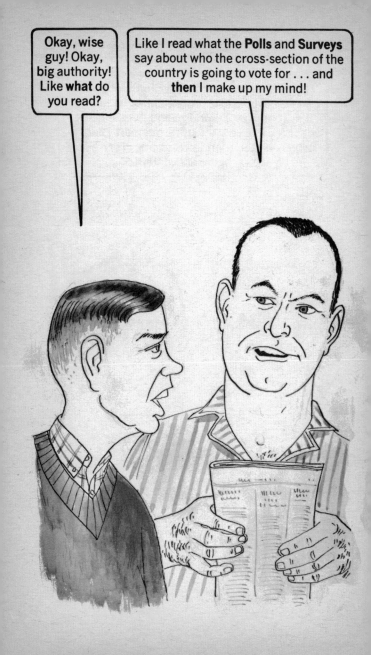

SEEING THE LIGHT

PET PEEVE

SWITCH IN TIME

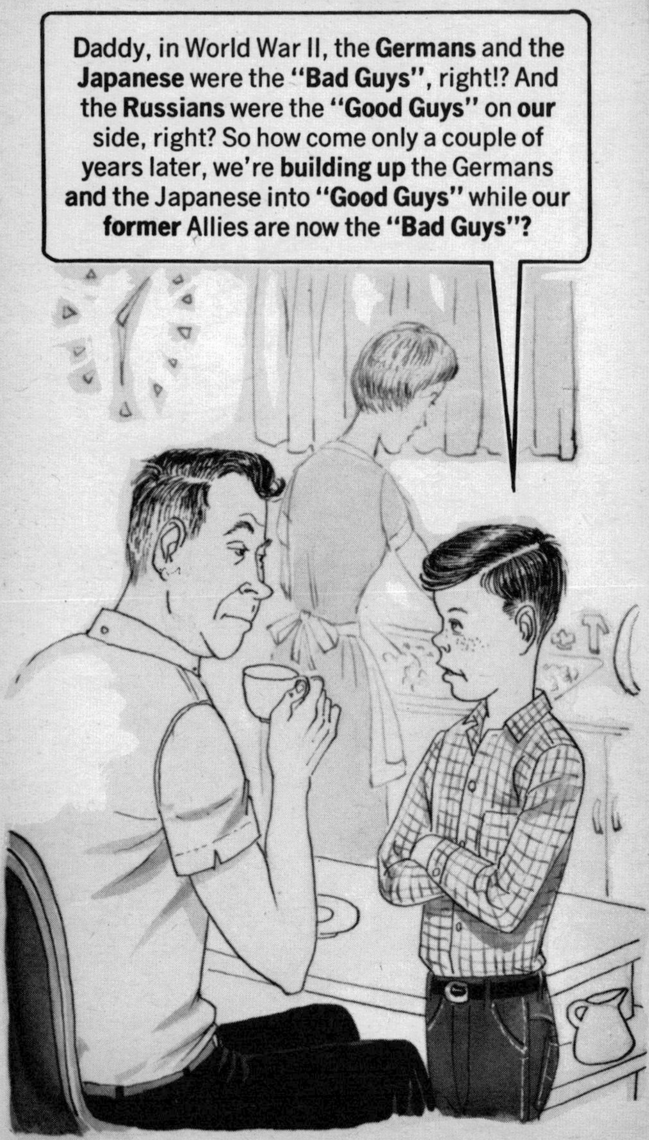

FORKED TONGUE-IN-CHEEK

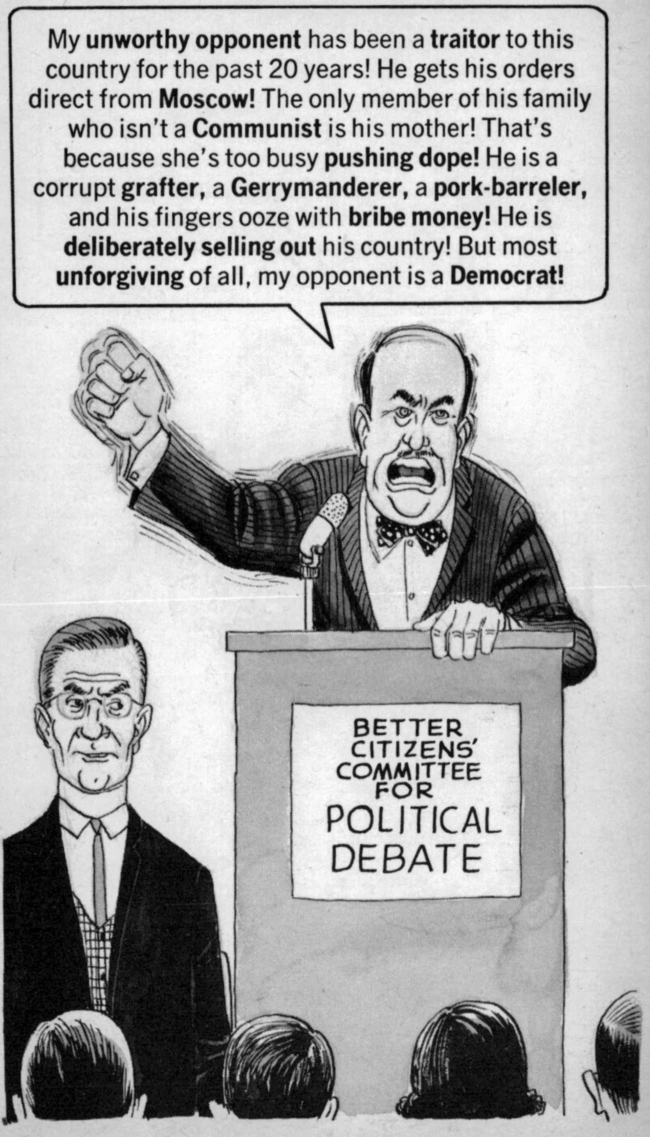